Gagging For It

by
Danny Sturrock

Gagging For It
by Danny Sturrock

Author's acknowledgments:

Mark Wheeller, thanks so much for all your hard work and support, it is very much appreciated. All at Oaklands Youth Theatre for your ongoing support and enthusiasm. To all at **dbda**, thank you for all the hard work you guys have put into this!

My family and friends who have supported me in my writing and tolerated having to listen to dance music for months on end! Thank you to Mandy for your love and support, it means a lot!

Finally, thank you to all of those groups that go on to use Gagging For it! – I hope you have as much fun working with this piece as I did writing it.

ISBN 978-1-902843-17-9

BRITISH LIBRARY CATALOGUING IN PUBLICATION DATA
A catalogue record for this book is available from the British Library.

Published by **dbda**, Pin Point, Rosslyn Crescent, Harrow HA1 2SU
First edition, published in 2004. Reprinted in 2007.

All enquiries regarding all rights associated with this play, including performing rights, should be addressed to:
Sophie Gorell Barnes, MBA Literary Agents Limited, 62 Grafton Way, London W1P 5LD.
Tel: 020 7387 2076   Fax: 020 7387 2042   E-mail: sophie@mbalit.co.uk

Further copies of this publication can be purchased from:
dbda, Pin Point, Rosslyn Crescent, Harrow HA1 2SU.
Tel: 0870 333 7771   Fax: 0870 333 7772   E-mail: info@dbda.co.uk

Dedicated to the memory of Nicky Chapman,
for whom the part of Tara was originally written.

Nicky played Tara throughout the first run of the
production and was truly amazing!

I hope your friendship, energy and sense of fun
will live on in *Gagging For It!*
We miss you dearly!

Chappers, this one's for you!

An introduction by Mark Wheeller

I am often asked to read scripts. I hardly have enough time to write my own plays and I don't particularly enjoy reading play scripts... so often don't get round to it... but I am always keen to see them in performance.

Danny Sturrock was the latest in a line of Sturrocks to pass through my hands at Oaklands Community School. They all gained high grades at GCSE Drama and were central players in the Oaklands Youth Theatre. Danny played a major role in **Chunnel of Love** and had wowed the crowds at the NSDF when we were asked to perform there in 1992. He left school after his GCSEs and although I had given him the lead role (Andy) in **Legal Weapon** his working hours clashed with Youth Theatre rehearsal times so he had to leave. I heard virtually nothing from him for three or so years when, as suddenly as he left, he returned to help on the technical side of **Wacky Soap**. Following that he took on the lead role of Rob in our production of **Sweet FA** (about another ex-student of mine who played football for Wimbledon Ladies.) The whole cast of Sweet FA went on a trip to the NSDF and this time it was Danny's time to be 'wowed' by what he saw. So much so he was inspired to write a play. People at Scarborough often say this... few get round to actually doing it! Four months later (following a holiday Dan took in Ibiza) Dan asked if I would like to look at the play he'd written. Knowing how I hate reading plays he added...

"and if you like it, I'll direct it and the Youth Theatre can present it."

It arrived by email on my computer at the start of the summer holidays. I delayed reading it but, after a week or so, began to feel guilty so printed it off on a sunny day and sat in the garden denying myself the book I was reading at the time (and enjoying!), to read it.

Obviously the title was the first thing I saw. I remember wishing that I'd thought of it first. I knew it was a winner and would instantly appeal to a teenage audience. However it also suggested a play that was going to be full of laughs. But would it? I couldn't get over the fact that it was written by an ex-pupil of mine... someone who'd shown an enthusiasm for Drama but never for writing plays. Even his final GCSE presentation had been a pre-written published play (The Last Laugh). Surely if Danny had such promise, he would have demonstrated it then, by opting to present a devised piece.

The first few pages were excellent... surprisingly so... really funny... laugh out loud funny and incredibly fast paced. This was amazing... could he keep it up? He managed to do something I have always found pretty much impossible... to have ongoing dialogue moving the story forward without any narrative voice. It was easy to envisage on stage. I knew OYT members would adore it. I don't think I had a break. I read it in one go (which is amazing for my short attention span). When I finished reading I couldn't wait to phone Danny and say how amazing I thought it was. It was even at that stage an inspired piece of work... and I say it again... really funny!

I too was planning a production so we held joint auditions. I felt there was quite a buzz about what I was doing (**Secrets in Love**) and no-one really knew anything about **Gagging For It.** However, each extract Danny had chosen for the audition worked amazingly well and got loud laughs from all of us who were watching. I can remember one section where I had that tingly feeling down my spine as we (the audience) were made to sympathise for Chris. I kept reminding myself that this was only the audition. **Gagging For It** was like a magnet... suddenly everyone wanted to be part of it. I remember thinking how the scripted extracts I had selected from my play, paled against those from Danny's. I subsequently altered my plans (**Secrets in Love** never saw the light of day) forcing **Gagging For It** to take centre stage.

I played virtually no part in Danny's rehearsals. Those cast members I taught, all spoke well of how it was going. If anything, their enthusiasm for the project increased as the performance date got closer. Three weeks before the opening night I was invited to see a run through. My expectations were high... so I was aware I could be in for a disappointment. When I arrived there were technical problems and the start time was delayed. For the first time since the audition night I began to worry. Had I allowed Danny too much freedom? He'd had no previous experience either as a director or writer. Should I have intervened more? Had I been unsupportive? What if it was a complete disaster? I knew I'd feel responsible. It's one thing to write a play, it's another to organise a group of young people and have the imagination to direct it.

I needn't have worried. It was fantastic! It had a quality of 'youth' that made me feel really old! Danny had produced a play that had a real future. The aspect that had not communicated itself to me (I hope it does in the published text) in the script (as I read it originally) was the importance of the choreographed sequences. They provided the moments of most imagination and provided outstanding highlights!

The production went on to be performed at our Oaklands Theatre and was received with great enthusiasm… it became 'cool' to go and see *Gagging For It*. It was even cooler for those who were in it! They became instant celebrities in the school. Soon after, the cast were on the One Act Play circuit. Here they met with more success, winning awards at every Festival they performed at!

Danny was still not entirely satisfied and decided to re-write sections of the play and in 2004 presented the new version which is pretty much what you have here in the **dbda** text. With a different cast it went on to clean up even more awards… again winning at least one award in every Festival it entered… surely proving that it was not only an excellent cast but a superb play.

In March 2004, Danny was approached by some Year 11 students at my school Oaklands Community in Southampton, who had seen the Youth Theatre production. They wanted to ask if he would allow them to use some of the play for their exam. Not only was he willing for this to happen but he offered to write a version lasting 30 minutes for six characters (3m/3f) to comply with the Edexcel GCSE exam criteria. This version proved how versatile Danny was willing to be with his work and also what a superb play *Gagging For It* is. It has inspired some outstanding performances from the six Year 11s (who went on to exceed our expectations by a long way in their GCSEs two of them achieving maximum marks… all achieving A's or A*s). All the examination plays were performed to our current Year 9. Although it was up against some stiff opposition, *Gagging For It* once again proved to be a firm favourite with the audience.

I approached **dbda** with the play in May following the exam. It took them two weeks to decide to publish! I am sure Danny has produced a play which will come to be a classic GCSE play and will also be used by schools up and down the country as a school production in the fight against drug misuse. Good luck to all who choose to work on this play. It requires absolute commitment from all the performers and a sense of fun throughout which is contrasted by the huge sense of loss at the end. Have fun with it! I'm gagging to see it again!

Gagging For It was premiered by
the Oaklands Youth Theatre '006'
on Thursday 18th March 2004
with the following cast:

Chris	Matt Savage
Kev	Martin Wiltshire
Jay	Darren Harley
Teresa	Katy Frecknall
Tara	Hollie Green
Bianca	Charlotte Wells
Crazy Dave/ Bazza	Sam Jolly
DJ / Danni	Matthew Griffiths
DJ 2	Anne-Marie Sturrock
Director	Danny Sturrock
Lighting Design, Multimedia and Sound	Danny Sturrock

Productions of *Gagging For It* should use minimal props and setting so that the pace of the play is not interrupted by lengthy scene changes. Scene changes should be incorporated into the scenes using choreographed sequences and/or underscored pre-recorded music.

The Oaklands Youth Theatre Production

Above:
The karaoke scene with Martin Wiltshire (Kev),
Darren Harley (Jay), Matt Savage (Chris),
Charlotte Wells (Bianca), Hollie Green (Tara)
and Katy Frecknall (Teresa).

Above and left:
Charlotte Wells (Bianca), Hollie Green (Tara)
and Katy Frecknall (Teresa) in the girls bedroom
and karaoke scenes.

Above:
The opening choreographed scene.

Right:
The lads getting ready (L to R) Martin Wiltshire (Kev), Matt Savage (Chris) and Darren Harley (Jay).

Left:
The girls getting ready to go out (L to R) Katy Frecknall (Teresa), Charlotte Wells (Bianca) and Hollie Green (Tara).

List of Characters

Gagging For It can be performed by a cast of 9 (3m/3f plus 3m or f) or as a cast of 4 (3m/3f) using the suggested cuts at the back of this book.

Cast List in order of appearance

Chris	A likeable seventeen year old, known to be a bit soft.
Bianca	Flirty and bubbly eighteen year old, a bit dizzy.
Teresa	A down to earth seventeen year old, kind, caring and clever.
Tara	Seventeen year old girl, bit of a tomboy, the loud one!
Jay	Eighteen year old, lager drinking layabout.
Kev	Eighteen year old ladies man, loves life, lager and the ladies!
Crazy Dave	Eighteen year old thug, but looks younger.
Danni	Twenty-four year old transvestite.
Bazza	Nineteen year old friend of Kev.
Doctor	Foreign, speaks in broken English.

Section 1: Coming down with a bump

The lights fade up as Chris enters, clearly anxious and distressed.
He sits on a block down stage right and is lit by a single spot light. He
produces a mimed mobile phone and nervously pinches in a number
and places it to his ear with a heavy sigh.

Chris:
(*Quickly cancelling the call before anyone answers.*)
Fuck!
(*Chris holds his head in his hands and tries to*
compose himself. After a moment he lifts his head
to address the audience.)
What a mess… I just didn't know what to say…
couldn't bring myself to do it. Bottled it! (*Pause*)
Knowing what had gone wrong and being part of
the problem… that's always been the hardest thing
to deal with…

(*Bianca enters stage left also in a state of disbelief.*)

Bianca:
Chris, have you called them?

Chris:
Not yet… I can't.

Bianca:
Do you want me to…

Chris:
It has to be me… it's the least I can do… where the
hell do I start though B?

Bianca:
Just start at the beginning.

(*The two actors on stage freeze as the lights fade to*
a blackout. They exit.)

Section 2: Gagging For It!

The lights quickly fade up to represent a smoke filled club.
Loud upbeat dance music plays (A mix of the Jungle Brothers –
Breathe, Don't Stop was used in the original production).
Kev, Chris, Jay, Teresa, Bianca and Tara enter the stage.

A short choreographed scene follows showing a typical night out
clubbing for the group. Elements of the night out could include,
Drinking, Dancing, Smoking, Flirting etc. This movement should be
stylised and give the overall impression of a fun group of young adults
without a care in the world. The sequence should end with a smooth
and quick scene change, which leads straight into the next section.

Section 3: Teresa's Bedroom

The music fades out and lights fade down across to Teresa's bedroom. Tara, Bianca and Teresa are getting ready to go out clubbing. Teresa is the quieter one of the three girls and could be viewed as the more sensible one. Tara, a tomboy up until a few years ago, is a bit louder and would rather down a pint of bitter than sip on a cocktail. However, behind the brash exterior, she is a very good friend to the other girls. Bianca is a total flirt. Her dress code is simply 'less is more'! Although a bit of a lightweight, she will not stop pulling blokes until she collapses!

Bianca:	Does my bum look big in this?
Teresa:	What d'ya say B?
Bianca:	My bum!... Does it look big in this?
Tara:	Your bum looks big in everything B. *(Teresa laughs.)*
Bianca:	Oh shut up Tara. No, seriously, does it look big to you?
T & T:	NO!
Bianca:	Really?
T & T:	YES Really!
Bianca:	No, you're right it does look big. I'll have to find something else.
Tara:	Oh hurry up B, you're cutting into my drinking time! *(Bianca exits.)*
Teresa:	I hope Chris is there tonight, he's so sweet!
Tara:	How would you know? You haven't had the bottle to speak to him yet!
Teresa:	So?
Tara:	So... if you like him that much, why don't you ask him out?
Teresa:	I can't!
Tara:	Why not?

Section 3

Teresa:	He's only gonna say no!
Tara:	Well you don't know until you try!
Teresa:	It's all right for you. You've got Jay!
Tara:	That ain't anything serious.
Teresa:	*(Shocked)* But you've slept with him?
Tara:	*(Loud)* It's just sex, Teresa.
Teresa:	*(Anxiously)* Keep ya voice down Tara, my mum's downstairs!
Tara:	*(Sarcastically)* Sorry!
Teresa:	Anyway… I'm saving myself for the right man.
Tara:	*(Loud)* Hang on... You mean you're a...
Teresa:	*(Cutting in)* ...Yes… a virgin. It's not a crime is it?
Tara:	No, but I just assumed you'd done it before.
Teresa:	When I do it, I want it to be special.
Tara:	That's what we all say. The chances are the first time will happen after a few drinks in the back of a Ford Escort or in a parent's bedroom at a party.
Teresa:	Well not me!
	(Bianca enters wearing a significantly shorter skirt!)
Bianca:	Do I look alright?
Tara:	Fine. Can we go please?
Bianca:	*(Bending over to pick up a jacket with the others behind her.)* Do you think it's too short?
T&T:	*(In fright)* Arrrrgggghhh!
Teresa:	*(Covering her eyes)* Perhaps just a little B!
Bianca:	Excellent! Right, handbag check ladies.

14

(The following dialogue should be spoken with the appropriate choral movement.)

Bianca:	Purses?
T & T:	Yep?
Teresa:	Hairbrush
T & B:	Got it!
Tara:	Shampoo and Conditioner?
All:	Nah, sod it!
Bianca:	Lipstick
Tara:	Eyeliner
Teresa:	Breath mints, Foundation
All:	For use in emergency situations
Teresa:	Mobile phones with plenty of credit
Bianca:	A spare set of knickers, *(with thrusting motion)* assuming I get it!
T & T:	Bianca!!!
Bianca:	What?
Teresa:	That's disgusting!
Bianca:	Sorry, but you have to be prepared. I might meet a right stud and end up spending the night at his place, and a girl needs clean underwear in the morning.
Tara:	Yeah alright, we ready then or what?
Bianca:	Yep.
Tara:	Let's get going then.
Teresa:	*(As she exits with the others)* I can't believe you take a spare pair of knickers out with you?

Section 3

The girls exit and the lights cross to the other side of stage. Music plays over the opening of the next scene (a remix of The Wise Guy's 'Ooh La La' was used in the original production). The lads enter in towels, Union Jack boxer's shorts underneath.

A short choreographed sequence follows. It should show the lads getting ready i.e. showering, shaving, changing perhaps with a bit of playful physical banter between them all. Kev and Jay then mime opening a couple of beers, downing them and crushing the cans. Chris (not wanting to feel left out) also tries it but can't open the can!

Jay:	*(Snatching the can)* Give it here! *(Jay goes to open the can for him and decides to shake it up a bit first. He then opens it, spraying the beer all over Chris.)*
Kev & Jay:	*(Laughing)* You thick twat!
Chris:	I ain't thick!
Kev & Jay:	All this coming from a guy who thought oral sex meant having a group discussion about it!
Chris:	We were kids! *(The lads continue getting ready.)*
Jay:	Oi lads, how's about a tequila before we shoot off?
Kev:	Good call Jay!
Chris:	We can't use the tequila, it's my dad's.
Jay:	Lighten up a bit will ya Chris.
Chris:	No seriously, he'll go spare if we drink any.
Kev:	Well, he'll never know will he... we'll just top it back up with water afterwards. Now shut up and pass me those glasses.
Chris:	*(Mumbling to himself as he mimes getting the glasses.)* I'm a dead man.
Kev:	Here you are. Get this down ya. Right get ready...

OK after four...

All: One, Two, Three, Four! Salt, Slam, Lemon, Arrggh!
                             *(All of their faces screw up from the taste of
                             the lemon.)*
                             Lovely ladies here we come!

*Dance music fades up and the lights quickly change to set the mood of
a nightclub. The stage is filled with smoke as the actors quickly set the
stage in role to resemble a nightclub.*

Section 4: The Lovers' Guide

The three lads enter the club and take a seat.

Jay:	Your round then Chris!
Chris:	How do you work that one out?
Jay:	Simple really. Your name comes first in the alphabet so you get the first round in. That's the rule!
Chris:	What kind of a stupid bloody rule is that?
Jay:	Well if it gets me my first drink free, then it's a bloody good one, now run along there's a good lad.
Chris:	Alright, what you havin'?
Jay:	Mine's a Pint of Smooth, cheers mate, oh… and keep the change!
Kev:	I'll give you a hand Chris.
	(Chris and Kev approach the bar.)
Kev:	How come you're so touchy tonight?
Chris:	Ah you know, just a bit stressed out what with our exams and Uni coming up.
Kev:	You what? Exam stress my arse!
Chris:	Well it is!
Kev:	Yeah right, I know that face, that's your "I'm pissed off coz I never pull face"
Chris:	Is not!
Kev:	Bloody is… so come on, spill it!
Chris:	Well… well, it's just gonna be the same old thing isn't it.
Kev:	What d'ya mean?
Chris:	I'll buy the drinks all night, you and Jay will get rat-arsed, pull a couple of birds, go back to theirs and I'll have to go home on my tod again.

18

Kev: See I knew it! Chrissy wants some action!

Chris: No, it's not that.

Kev: Well what then?

Chris: There's this girl…

Kev: *(Interrupting)* I knew it!

Chris: Kev! She seems really nice, not that I've actually had the bottle to speak to her yet, but she just stands out from the crowd, you know?

Kev: What, you mean she's pig ugly?

Chris: No!

Kev: A big bertha?!

Chris: No!

Kev: She's got a huge hooter?

Chris: Kev! She's… oh… I don't know what I mean.

Kev: Who is she? Do I know her? *(Chris stays silent.)* I do don't I? Come on then spill it!

Chris: It's Teresa.

Kev: Why didn't you say before? I'll have a word with Tara for ya.

Chris: No Kev, I want to do it my way alright? It's just… I'm not that good with women. What do I say?

Kev: Right, listen up!
(Kev clicks his fingers and the lighting and music changes to set the mood for Lurve! [sic] Marvin Gaye's Let's Get It On was used in the original production.)

Chris: What you doing?

Kev: It is time for a few lessons in the art of pulling my friend!

Section 4

Chris:	This is stupid!
Kev:	Lesson 1: The look. Eye contact plays a vital part of the pulling technique and for the purpose of this exercise, I will play the woman. Right, now give me a look that says "Hey babe, You look hot!"
	(Chris screws up his face trying to mimic Kev.)
Kev:	OK, Chris that's more of a Quasimodo look. Try not to look so... umm... deranged alright!
Chris:	See, I told you this was stupid...
Kev:	Ye who hath little faith my friend! Let's try it again, but this time, just pretend that you look impressed at a new car someone has just bought.
	(Chris pulls off a look that is what Kev wanted.)
Kev:	That's good! That's really good! Right... now... whenever you see Teresa just look her up and down and think... "Hey baby, nice car!" Ok?
Chris:	I guess so!
Kev:	OK, Lesson 2: The approach. When you decide to go up to Teresa, you can't just run up to her coz that makes you look desperate... and don't follow her around either, as that will probably scare her off. Pick a moment when she is still, and after you've made the initial eye contact make your move. Just take a cool steady walk over to her and keep that eye contact at all times, got it?
Chris:	I guess so!
Kev:	Right, now this is the most important lesson of all. Lesson 3: The Chat Up Line. Now don't use any lines like "Do you come here often", as they just don't work. Say something like... "Hi, I've been watching you for some time and I just had to come over. You look absolutely stunning; can I buy you a

drink?" She'll be putty in your hands after that mate! Trust me.

Chris: What if she just laughs at me?

Kev: She won't mate. Look… just pretend Jay is Teresa and do exactly what I told you, then me and Jay can tell you what we think, OK?

Chris: OK, here goes.

(Kev whistles at Jay and points to Chris. Chris is doing all that Kev has taught him, however Jay looks a bit concerned.)

Jay: Chris, why are you looking at me like that… pack it in will ya!

(Chris leans next to Jay.)

Chris: Hi, I have been watching you for some time and I just had to come over. You look absolutely stunning; can I buy you a drink?

(The action switches into slow-mo. Chris looks round at Kev for approval and Kev gives him the thumbs up, then as he turns round Jay knees Chris in the groin. They freeze. All of these movements and facial expressions should be exaggerated for comic effect.)

(Suddenly the action returns to normal speed. Chris falls to his knees, clutching his groin as Kev runs over to speak to Jay.)

Kev: What the hell did you do that for?

Jay: He was trying to chat me up!

Kev: No! You've got it all wrong mate. I told him to test his chatting up technique out on you.

Jay: How the bloody hell was I supposed to know?

Kev: Look… help me get him up will ya.

Section 4

(The lads freeze where they are and the lights crossfade to the other side of the stage where Tara and Teresa enter.)

Teresa: We're not going to be out all night, are we Tara, you know… with final exams and everything tomorrow?

Tara: Are you being serious? What you worrying about them for, I'm not! Anyway, you always pass everything!

Teresa: Well yeah but I usually revise the night before, and if I drink too much I might forget it all.

Tara: Will you lighten up! What would you prefer, your face stuck in a book all night or some cute guy attached to your face all night!

Teresa: Yeah, good point! Anyway… I can always get up a bit early and revise then!

Tara: *(Talking to Bianca who is off stage.)* B will you put him down, there's plenty of time for that later.

Bianca: *(From off stage)* I'll see you later… Oh, cheeky

Teresa: Oh no! There's Chris, see… told you this was a bad idea!

Bianca: Cooor girls, did you get a look at him! (Mimes grabbing his backside.) Buttocks tighter than Ebenezer Scrooge!

(Kev and Jay notice the girls and immediately drop Chris back on the floor.)

Kev: Evenin' ladies, *(To Bianca)* Hey B, is that a ladder in your tights or is it a stairway to heaven?

Bianca: Cheeky git!

Jay: Tara!

Tara: Jay!

Jay: What you drinking?

Tara:	I'll have half a pint if you're offering.
Jay:	HALF a pint? What of larger?
Tara:	Behave! Vodka!
Jay:	Good girl! *(Jay and Tara go over to the bar.)*
Bianca:	Aren't you gonna offer me a drink then Kev?
Kev:	Yeah, course I am! Come on. *(Bianca and Kev go over to the bar, leaving Chris and Teresa alone. Chris is now stood up but still clutching his groin. As Chris and Teresa start talking the rest of the group look on, in the hope that Chris won't mess things up!)*
Teresa:	You alright?
Chris:	*(Embarrassed)* Yeah I'm fine thanks!
Teresa:	What happened?
Chris:	It's stupid really, Kev was giving me lessons on how to... *(He realises who he's talking to)...* uh... lessons on how to... uh... do you come here often? *(The group each slap their foreheads in sync and mutter under their breath.)*
TBK&J:	Doh!
Teresa:	What? You know I do! You see me every week!
Chris:	Yeah I know, sorry.
Teresa:	Sure you're alright?
Chris:	Positive!
Teresa:	How come you've never spoken to me before?
Chris:	I dunno... well... you're a girl aren't you?
Teresa:	Are you saying I look like a bloke?
Chris:	No, obviously you're a girl! I mean you wouldn't

have big old jubblies if you were a bloke would you? What I mean is…

Teresa: Oi, what you doing looking at my boobs?

Chris: What? I wasn't! Why would I wanna look at your boobs? I wouldn't wanna look at your boobs!

Teresa: What's wrong with them?

Chris: Nothing… nothing at all. They're really nice… I'd even pay to see 'em!

(Teresa takes offence and slaps Chris.)

Chris: Will people please stop hitting me! Teresa wait! You've got it all wrong! *(Under his breath)* I'm just trying to tell you that… I fancy you.

(Teresa walks off, not hearing Chris say he fancies her. Kev sees that Teresa is furious and walks over to Chris.)

Kev: What the hell did you say to Teresa? She's got a right face on.

Chris: I was trying to chat her up!

Kev: Chat her up! Anyone would think that you just asked to see her jugs or something!

Chris: Do I look that stupid?

Kev: Do you want me to answer that? Come on! Redeem yourself on the dance floor.

(A club track plays as they are all dancing. Chris turns out to be the worst dancer in the world and has no sense of rhythm!)

Kev: *(Pulling Chris off of the dance floor.)* That's enough of that!

Chris: What?

(The stage darkens as the music continues; the girls and Jay all exit the stage. Kev and Chris are outside the club waiting for Jay, it is the end of the evening. Jay is off stage and has started an argument with Crazy Dave in the club.)

Chris: Come on Jay, I wanna get home.

Kev: *(To Chris)* What the hell did you think you were doing in there?

Chris: What do you mean? Those were some of my best moves. I mean I had the funky chicken, and the whole wiggly arm thing going on…

Kev: OK stop! No one needs to see that again.

Chris: Everyone used to love it when I did it at parties.

Kev: When you were six! Your dance moves went out with the Shell Suit!

Chris: It wasn't that bad!

Kev: No, it was worse, and if you ever do that again, while you're out clubbing with me, I'm going to kill you! I've got a reputation to keep…
(aside) Come on Jay.

Section 5: Chucking out and up time

Jay:	*(As he enters shouting off stage)* Oi, What did you call me? Well come on then big man let's have it!
C & K:	Oh Bollocks!
Chris:	Here we go again.
	(Jay appears on stage followed by Crazy Dave.)
Crazy Dave:	*(Enters from off stage.)* You heard me! You want to watch who you're talking to!
Jay:	Do you seriously think you can take all three of us on?
Crazy Dave:	Do you seriously think you three can take me on?
Kev:	What?
Crazy Dave:	What?
Chris:	Listen Mate, why don't you just go back inside before you get hurt?
Crazy Dave:	Why don't you lot go back inside before you get hurt?
Kev:	Will you stop repeating everything we say?
Crazy Dave:	Will you stop repeating everything I say?
Kev:	Wha... look ju... jus... Jay tell him!
Jay:	Don't say I didn't warn you mate!
Crazy Dave:	Don't say I didn't warn you!
Chris:	He's doing it again!
Kev:	Right prepare to get your head kicked in!
Crazy Dave:	Very well! *(Crazy Dave takes up a Karate like stance and stays frozen, eyes closed and begins humming a single note.)*
Jay:	What's he doing now?

26

Chris:	This guy's a bloody fruitcake!
Kev:	Just hit him!
Jay:	My pleasure.
Crazy Dave:	Oh, just a second! Did I mention that I know every martial art known to mankind?
C, J & K:	Yeah right!

(A 'Matrix' style choreographed fight scene to music now follows. A mix of The Prodigy's – Smack My Bitch Up was used in the original production. This fight scene should be choreographed using slow motion and a lot of exaggerated facial expression and movement. It should end with the lads being defeated and hobbling off stage. As they exit the girls enter. The lights fade across to stage left where Tara and Teresa are sitting in Teresa's bedroom again, talking. Bianca can be heard throwing up off stage.)

Teresa:	You alright in there B? *(Bianca throws up again as Teresa and Tara wince.)*
Tara:	Lightweight... if it wasn't for her getting so pissed we could have stayed at the club longer.
Teresa:	I told her not to have those Tequilas! She best not throw up on my mum's new bathroom rug, she'll kill me! *(Bianca can be heard throwing up again.)*
Bianca:	*(Off stage giggling slightly.)* Oops, missed.
Teresa:	B! Will you watch where you're puking!
Tara:	You've got to hand it to the girl though, even though she had lost sense of sight and speech she still managed to pull five more blokes before passing out in the lavvy's!
Teresa:	I don't know how she does it. Not one bloke so much as even looked at me tonight.
Tara:	What you talking about? I saw you flirting with Chris.

Teresa:	I was not!
Tara:	You so were! So, how did it go? Did he tell you he fancies you?
Teresa:	No! I thought he was going to at one point, but then he said I looked like a bloke and asked to see my boobs! Are you sure he really likes me?
Tara:	Are you kidding? He's gagging for it!
Teresa:	It didn't seem like it to me.
Tara:	Teresa, trust me!
	(Bianca enters still looking a bit off colour.)
	Right, who's up for a nice greasy bacon sandwich! *(She rises.)*
	(Bianca heaves at the thought of it and bolts back out to the bathroom and can be heard heaving again!)
Teresa:	Not on the rug!
Tara:	*(Looking off stage.)* Too late!

Section 6: Schools Out!

The lights fade to black. An alarm clock can then be heard to signal a new day as the lighting fades back up.
Kev, Chris, Jay, Tara, Teresa and Bianca stagger onto stage, still half asleep not realising what the time is!

All: Shit, we're late!

(The following section should be choreographed to music. A Soul Wax mix of Dolly Parton's 'Nine till Five' was used in the original production. This sequence should show Kev, Chris, Tara, Teresa and Bianca rushing around getting ready to go to college, travelling to college – some running for buses, some riding bikes – and then arriving at college and sitting down for their exams. Jay doesn't go to college and just spends his time sitting in his house watching daytime telly and can just keep getting in people's way in this section. As the music fades perhaps the following lines could all be recorded and played through the speakers as if they were their thoughts – alternatively they could be spoken by someone off stage. All of Jay's lines should be spoken and not recorded!)

Bianca: *(As if thinking aloud whilst sitting an exam.)* Tight perm, frizzy perm, afro perm, poodle perm and... um... *(Unsure and hitting herself on the head.)* Oh come on brain... permy perm? Oh that'll do!

Kev: *(Sitting in his exam.)* My life is over, my mum's gonna kill me! *(Looking around the class.)* I mean, how the hell am I supposed to know what the average population of Outer Mongolia was between 1860 and 1960 *(In surprise)* Whoa!... I can see right down Debbie Jackson's top from here! Hang on, she's flirting with me! The little minx, OK Kev, keep it smooth, nice and smooth. *(Turns to face the imaginary Debbie and does a cheesey 'Grrrrr' noise complete with claw and facial expression!)*

Jay: *(Sitting in his living room.)* Who needs college and uni, when you can be a graduate of the university of life. Now who do we have for today's lecture... *(Miming using a TV remote)*

29

Section 6

Weyhey, it's Richard & Judy... I'd shag her!

Tara: *(Nodding off to sleep and bashing her head on the desk which wakes her and startles her. She has a 'Post It' note stuck to her forehead: THE THEORY OF RELATIVITY!!!!!!! Realising what she has just done...)*
Oh my god, I've been asleep, it's OK, I don't think anyone noticed!

Teresa: Ooh, I know this, and this one, and this one, and that one, and that one, and that one, god everyone knows that!

Chris: I don't know that!!!!!!! Oh my god, I've forgotten everything, not only is Teresa going to think that I'm a breast obsessed womaniser, she's gonna think I'm an A Level failing loser too! ...I wonder if... what her breasts are like?...Chris!

(Each character repeats the above lines a further two times simultaneously as the music fades up again over the top. The music and lights fade out and then a single light quickly snaps back up, lighting just Jay.)

Jay: I'd shag that Richard too!

(Music fades back up to cover a short scene transition in which six blocks are stack to become a pool table in a pub. The girls exit the stage. The lads are in a pub. Chris and Jay are playing pool, and Kev is sat down flicking through holiday brochures.)

Kev: So boys... time to start sorting out the first of many Lads holidays! What do you think about Lanzarote?

Chris: You know what they call Lanzarote don't you? Lanzatotty!

Jay: More like Lanzagrotty! I ain't going there, I hate the place.

Chris: My mum would never let me go there anyway.

Jay: What you always worrying about your parents for?

Chris: Well they are paying half of this holiday for me. *(Jay shakes his head in disbelief.)*

Kev: Well what about Tenerife?

Jay: How much?

Kev: One week, all-inclusive, based on four people sharing with wc, balcony and view of the beach...

Jay: Kev! Just tell me how much!

Kev: £700. *(Or whatever a current 'high' price may be for such a holiday.)*

Jay: £700! I could go to Jamaica for that price!

Kev: Yeah, but it's got a sunken pool bar and everything!

Jay: I don't care if it's got en suite Juggling Monkeys, there's no way I am paying £700 for one week of sun!

Chris: It is a bit steep Kev.

Kev: Yeah s'pose! *(He continues flicking through the brochure.)*

Jay: Tara and that lot are going to Ibiza this year, now I wouldn't mind some of that!

Chris: You're a genius Jay!

Jay: What?

Chris: Well my mum works with Tara's mum and if my mum knows that Tara is going to, then she's bound to let me go too!

Jay: Will you please shut up about your parents!

Kev: Well why don't we go? We could arrange to meet up with them, *(To Chris)* and it would give you a chance to get better acquainted with Teresa if you catch my drift.

Chris:	She's not like that!
Kev:	Trust me mate get a few drinks inside her, take her for a midnight stroll along the beach and she will be like that!
Chris:	You think so?
Kev:	Mate, I know so! So, what do you think?
Chris:	Sounds good to me.
Kev:	Jay?
Jay:	Be a laugh I suppose, alright then count me in.
Chris:	Sound. I'll phone Tara and see what she thinks.

(The lights come up on Teresa's bedroom. They are working out to a Yoga video. All of them are bent up in bizarre positions on the floor. Tara's mobile phone rings.)

Tara:	I thought this was supposed to be relaxing!
Bianca:	There is no way I can get my leg up there!
Teresa:	Arrgh, help will ya... I think I'm stuck! *(The others start laughing.)*
Teresa:	I'm serious, I'm really stuck.
Tara:	*(Answering the phone)* Hello?
	(As the phone call starts, all that Chris can hear is that Tara is out of breath. He can also hear the girls screaming and panting in the background.)
Chris:	Hi Tara, it's Chris.
Tara:	Alright Chris, you ol' tart, how's it going?
Chris:	Not so bad thanks! What's that noise?
Tara:	What noise?
Chris:	You watching porn?
Tara:	Oh that, that's just Teresa and Bianca rolling around

on the floor!

Chris:	*(To Jay and Kev)* Oi lads, the girls are having some kinda lesbian orgy!
Jay:	Are they hell as like!
Chris:	No, straight up, Tara just said! Here, listen! *(Kev picks up the phone.)*
Teresa:	*(Instructing Bianca, who is trying to free her leg.)* Oh yeah, that's it, come on, Harder, Harder! Ooooh yeah, that's it!
Kev:	He's right!
Tara:	Chris?
Kev:	Alright Tara it's Kev! You never told us that you three were natives of the magical island of Lesbos!
Tara:	What you going on about Kev?
Kev:	Chris said you lot are having some kinda threesome, and don't deny it coz we could all hear the panting!
Tara:	What?! You wish! We're doing Yoga!
Kev:	*(Handing the phone back to Chris)* They're not having a lesbian sex fest! They're doing yoga you Muppet!
Chris:	Sorry! *(To Tara)* Hiya,
Tara:	What was all that about?
Chris:	Never mind. Anyway, the reason I called is because me and the lads have been thinking…
Tara:	*(Interrupting)* Blimey, did it hurt?
Chris:	Very funny! You and the girls are planning to go to Ibiza this year aren't you?
Tara:	Yeah?
Chris:	Well, me and the lads are just looking through some holiday brochures and…

Section 6

Tara:	*(Interrupting again)* ...and you want to tag along?
Chris:	How did you know?
Tara:	I didn't! Bianca suggested the same thing earlier.
Chris:	What do you think then?
Tara:	Yeah, we're all up for it, especially Teresa. *(To Teresa)* Isn't that right?
Teresa:	Shut up Tara.
Chris:	Excellent! It'll be a cracking laugh!
All:	Ibiza here we come!

The lights dim slightly as music fades up to cover the scene transition. The music then fades out and the lights fade up to reveal the group sitting in an airport waiting lounge.

Section 7: Ibiza, here we come!

All tannoy announcements were recorded in the original production but could be spoken by someone off stage, perhaps through a microphone. The Bing Bong's should be spoken whether pre-recorded or not!

Tannoy: BING BONG! All passengers for flight number LX-137-Z to Los Angeles please make your way to gate number 27 for boarding, thank you. BING BONG!

Chris: I love flying! It's the best way to travel if you ask me!

Bianca: Yeah me too.

Teresa: I hate the take off. At least when you are coming in to land if there is a problem with the plane you won't have so far to fall.
(Kev looks increasingly worried.)

Tara: True.

Bianca: Did you know that you are more likely to die in car crash than in an aeroplane?

Teresa: Really?

Bianca: Yeah, I saw it on the telly once.

Jay: There's one thing that I could never understand about plane crash procedures. You know they tell you get into that position with your head between your legs! Well what bloody use is that going to be when you're hurtling towards the ground at 300mph in a steel tube? I reckon they should get everyone to stand up and the second before impact everyone should jump... that way the plane would hit the ground but the passengers wouldn't!

(Kev starts to hyperventilate.)

Chris: I don't think it quite works like that Jay!

Bianca: I don't know why they don't give everyone parachutes, that way no one would have to die!

Jay: No, that's no good, because as you jumped out of

the plane you'd get sucked into the engines.

Kev: SHUT UP! SHUT UP! SHUT UP! *(He is breathing heavily and needs his inhaler.)*

Teresa: What's up with him?

All: He's scared of flying.

Jay: *(Trying to give Kev an inhaler.)* Come on Kev, it's all right… deep breath… and again… that's it. Now find a happy place… find a happy place!

Kev: Find a happy place… find a happy place…

Tannoy: BING BONG! Passengers for flight number GR-745-T to Ibiza, please make you way to gate number 6 where your plane is now boarding, thank you. BING BONG!

Jay: This is us guys, come on Kev, it will be alright, and in a couple of hours we'll be in sunny Ibiza.

Kev: Find a happy place… find a happy place…

Jay: That's right mate… find a happy place!

(They all exit the stage as the lights fade to black. Appropriate music should fade up to cover this brief scene change.)

Kev: Find a happy place… find a happy place… find a happy place… find a happy place…

Jay: Kev, calm down!

Kev: Find a happy place… find a happy place!

(The lights come back up and Kev, Jay, Chris, Tara, Teresa and Bianca are grouped together sunbathing on a beach in Ibiza.)

Kev: This is the life ain't it?

Bianca: Too right!

Jay: No parents!

Gagging For It# Gagging For It

Chris:	No more exams!
Tara:	Shame we're only here for a week though.
Teresa:	Yeah.
All:	*(Relaxing sighs)* Ahhh!
Jay:	That cloud looks like a rabbit.
Tara:	What?
Jay:	That cloud... it looks just like a rabbit.
Bianca:	It doesn't look anything like a rabbit... more like a Volkswagen Beetle.
Teresa:	What are you lot on?
Chris:	Haven't you ever done this?
Teresa:	Done what?
Chris:	If you look at the clouds long enough you start to see all sorts of shapes in them... look at that one... a spitting image of a pineapple.
Kev:	That is so not a pineapple! More Like a Volkswagen Beetle!
Chris:	Guys, we still haven't sorted out where we are going tonight?
Bianca:	How about The Ministry... Manumission?
Jay:	No! They cost a fortune to get into.
Tara:	Why don't we just have a walk round and see what looks good then, yeah?
Chris:	Fine by me.
Kev:	Me too.
Tara:	Well I am going to head back and get something to eat. Gotta line my stomach for tonight! Are you lot coming?
Kev:	Yeah I suppose we might as well, come on lads.

Section 7

Chris:	Actually guys I am going to just lie here a bit longer and get some shut-eye.
Bianca:	Suit yourself.
Teresa:	*(Trying not to make it obvious she wants to be alone with Chris.)* Actually I might stop here for a bit too.
Bianca:	You can't! I need you to straighten my hair for me!
Teresa:	*(Trying to be subtle with clenched teeth and winks.)* Well, that's OK, I can do that when I get back B... can't I?
Bianca:	Why do you keep winking at me... Have you got sand in your eye?
Teresa:	*(Giving in)* Alright! I'm coming... *(Turning to Chris)* See you later Chris.
Chris:	*(A bit disappointed that Teresa's not staying with him)* Yeah, later!
Kev:	See you back at the apartment mate.
	(The others exit the stage as Chris gets comfortable and starts to fall asleep. He mumbles as he does so.)
Chris:	*(Talking to himself)* So is tonight gonna be the night Chris my lad? I do believe it shall. *(He starts day-dreaming.)* Tonight Matthew, I am going to be... Dr Lurve! *(Mumbling)* I have got to impress her, really impress her...

(The lighting changes to show Chris day-dreaming as the theme from 'Baywatch' fades up. Teresa appears and pretends to be drowning mouthing the words "Help, Please somebody help me". Chris jumps to his feet and produces some mimed binoculars from his towel. Chris then makes a melodramatic, slow motion, 'Baywatch' style rescue.)

Chris:	*(In a heroic US accent)* Are you OK ma'am?
Teresa:	You saved my life, how can I ever repay you?
Chris:	*(Returning to his normal voice.)* Well I suppose a

shag tonight is out of the question? *(He cowers expecting to be hit!)*

Teresa: *(Embracing Chris)* Anything for you my hero!

Chris: *(Can't believe his luck)* Result!

(Teresa gets up and slowly walks off blowing kisses to her hero. Chris lays back to how he was when he fell asleep. Fx. Water. The lighting suddenly changes to a deep blue as Chris opens his eyes to realise that the tide has come in and he has drifted out to sea!)

Chris: *(Still with his eyes closed.)* Oh, it's getting a bit nippy, think I'll put my top on and head back… where's my top gone?… and why is everything wet… oh! Please no, don't say I've drifted out on my lilo… *(He slowly opens one eye at a time and then turns to the audience with a look of horror on his face when he realises all he can see is sea!)* Arrrgggghhhhh!

Section 8: Expensive Clubs are a Drag!

The lighting quickly changes to depict night. The group are queuing up outside a popular Ibiza nightclub. Kev and Jay are laughing about Chris' drifting incident.

Kev:	*(Talking to Chris as they enter.)* Ah mate, you are funny. So what happened after that?
Chris:	Well, then I was picked up by the coast guard. *(Kev and Jay burst out laughing again.)*
Chris:	It wasn't funny!
Jay:	*(Still trying not to laugh)* Nah, you're right mate, I'm sorry… maybe you should just LIE-LO for a while!… get it… LI-LO! *(Kev and Jay burst out laughing again.)*
Chris:	Oh piss off the pair of ya!
Teresa:	Yeah, leave him alone! *(Moving closer to Chris.)* It must have been awful.
Chris:	*(Trying to milk the sympathy from Teresa.)* Yeah it was.
Bianca:	Anyway, are we going in or what?
Kev:	Well how much is it?
Tara:	40 quid.
Kev:	*(In horror)* 40 quid!!!!!!
Jay:	Kev, calm down. It's supposed to be a good club!
Kev:	*(Still in horror)* …but 40 quid! That's the equivalent of about 20 pints!
Tara:	Actually, it's only about 5. A pint in here will cost you about a fiver too!
Kev:	Five quid! For one measly pint! You're having a giraffe!
Teresa:	Oh come on Kev, you've already got us thrown out of nearly every other club.

(A girl [Danni] struts past the lads and enters the club. Danni is not actually a girl, but is a convincing transvestite. However, only Jay has realised this and sets out to stitch Kev up!)

Jay: *(To Kev)* Oi Oi Kev! Check out that totty my son!

Kev: I told you, I'm not paying 40 quid to get into a club... not for anything.

Jay: *(Tapping Kev to get his attention.)* Kev... KEV LOOK!

Kev: *(Annoyed)* What! *(notices Danni)* Just look at the jugs on that! Now that... THAT is well worth 40 quid.

Chris: Where you going?

Kev: We're going in.

Chris: But it's 40 quid!

Kev: Chris, don't be a twat! Just get ya wallet out!

              (Music then fades up as the group dance into the club.)

Tara: We're just going to the toilets, so we'll see you in a minute.

Chris: No worries.

(The girls go over to stage right and freeze as the lads take a seat. Danni is sitting to the far right of stage on her own.)

Chris: *(As if talking to himself)* Why do girls always go to the loos together?

Jay: *(Laughing to himself)* Oi Kev, there's that bird!

Kev: Where?

Jay: Over there! Bet you can't pull her!

Kev: Fifty quid says that I can!

Jay: *(Still laughing)* Fifty quid hey! Well if you're that sure, let's make it eighty!

Section 8

Kev:	Alright then, you're on!
Jay:	*(Still laughing)* Sucker!
Kev:	What are you laughing at?
Jay:	Nothing mate… now go on, what're you waiting for?
Kev:	Easy money! *(Kev slowly walks over to Danni.)*
Jay:	Now we can sit back and wait!
Chris:	What you on about?
Jay:	You'll see!
	(The lighting switches to stage right as Kev approaches Danni.)
Kev:	*(Leaning over behind Danni to whisper in her ear.)* Excuse me miss, I am a British Intelligence Agent from MI5. No! Don't look round. I have reason to believe that your life may be in danger. You must go back home immediately and await my instructions. *(Mimes pulling a pen and paper from his pocket.)* Here, write your telephone number on this piece of paper and I'll contact you later this evening. Your life may depend on it! *(Danni grabs hold of Kev's hand over her shoulder but does not look at him.)*
Kev:	Wow, that's some grip for a little lady!
Danni:	Listen mate, I appreciate the effort and everything but if you want my number your gonna have to try a bit harder than that!
Kev:	And what a deep voice you have!
Danni:	*(Turning round to face Kev.)* Look, do you want my number or not!
Kev:	*(In horror)* Arrrrgggghh! You're a bloke… *(Looking her up and down)*… no, you're a… what the hell are you?

Danni:	Don't be shy... hey, you're actually kinda cute! *(Moving in to kiss him.)*
Kev:	Oh no you don't! You stay back... *(Takes up a karate pose)*... I know... origami! *(Backing off towards the guys.)*
Danni:	*(Laughing as she exits stage.)* Your loss sweetheart. I won't lose sleep over it!
	(Kev joins the lads again who are laughing hysterically.)
Kev:	Not a word alright?
Chris:	You should have seen your face!
Kev:	You knew all long you git!
Jay:	Mate, I had no idea she was a geezer! Now where's my eighty quid!
Kev:	*(Mimes pulling money from his pocket.)* Git!
Chris:	You've got to see the funny side though mate!
	(Tara, Teresa and Bianca enter carrying drinks.)
Teresa:	Drinks are served boys!
Bianca:	What's so funny?
Chris:	You should have seen it. Kev was only just trying to ch... *(Kev kicks Chris to shut him up.)*
Kev:	Just laughing about a joke that Chris just told!
Teresa:	Let's hear it then.
Kev:	No. It was crap!
Teresa:	OK.
Bianca:	Right, last one to down their tequilas gets the next lot in.
Teresa:	You can count me out, I have had enough tonight already!

Section 8

Tara:	I'll have hers then!
Chris:	I'm all alright too cheers, if I have any more alcohol tonight, I'm gonna puke!
Kev:	Oh come on Chris, you're always such a girl!
Tara:	*(To Kev)* Oi!
Jay:	You're on holiday mate, live a little!
Bianca:	Yeah come on Chris. What's the point of coming to Ibiza if your not going to get plastered!
Kev:	I don't know what's the matter with ya… oh yeah I do, Teresa's blown you out hasn't she.
Jay:	Blown him out, he hasn't even told her he fancies her yet!
Teresa:	What?
Chris:	*(Storming off)* Jay! Thanks a lot mate. Make me look like a complete tosser, why don't ya.
Teresa:	*(Shouting)* Chris! *(To Jay)* Do you know what, you can be a right moron sometimes!
	(Teresa goes after Chris.)
Jay:	What did I say?
Bianca:	Just ignore it, they'll calm down. You never know, they might actually get together now!
Tara:	Come on, just get these down ya.
All:	One, two, three, Drink! *(they all down their slammers.)*

Section 9: Teresa makes her move

The lights fade to the other side of stage as appropriately romantic music fades gently over the top of the next section. (The Candlelight Mix of DJ Sammy's 'Heaven' was used in the original production.) Teresa sits down beside Chris on the opposite side of stage.

Teresa:	Are you OK?
Chris:	Jay and that just get on my tits sometimes ya know?
Teresa:	I know what you mean. *(Pause)*
Chris:	Look Teresa, just ignore what Jay said back there, OK.
Teresa:	What if I don't want to ignore it?
Chris:	I think it's better just to forget it… and carry on with what's left of the holiday.
Teresa:	Don't you fancy me then?
Chris:	What's the point? You're not interested in me!
Teresa:	How do you know?
Chris:	The last time I tried to chat you up, you slapped me!
Teresa:	You asked me to get my baps out!
Chris:	I just got embarrassed… confused… it wasn't what I meant.
Teresa:	Well?
Chris:	Well what?
Teresa:	I'm here now, aren't I? Why don't you try it again?
Chris:	What? You mean…
Teresa:	I mean… I might be willing to consider your offer!
Chris:	What… you mean… but I don't… um… alright then… err…
Teresa:	*(Laughing)* You're really bad at this aren't you?

Section 9

Chris:	Sorry, it's just that... *(Teresa interrupts Chris by grabbing him by the shirt and planting a kiss on him.)*
Chris:	Well, I wasn't expecting that! I could stay here with you all night...
Teresa:	What's stopping us?
Chris:	That lot? *(The lights switch across to the others who all give a cheesy wave, and then switch back.)*
Teresa:	Look, why don't we spend the day together at the fair in the town tomorrow, just me and you, then we can forget about them for a while... what do you say?
Chris:	Won't they all get funny with us?
Teresa:	They'll be too hung-over... I doubt they could stomach fairground rides.
Chris:	Alright then, you're on! But in the meantime, I'll have a bit more of this if you don't mind! *(Chris kisses Teresa.)*
Teresa:	Easy tiger!
Chris:	Grrrrrrrrrr! *(Doing a tiger impression.)* *(The couple starts tickling one another, laughing.)*
Teresa:	Oi naughty! *(The lights briefly fade to black.)*

Section 10: The Morning after

The music fades up as the cast set the next scene. The lights fade over to the other side of the stage, as the next scene starts with Chris and Teresa coming back to the apartment in the morning. There are bodies everywhere as the group wakes up. The music fades out.

Kev:	*(Laid on the sofa talking in his sleep.)* No Mum, I don't wanna go to school… why… all right, I'm up, *(Chris and Teresa creep in)* can I have some breakfast first?… I want some eggies and little soldiers in my special Fireman Sam eggcup… thanks mum… I love my eggies… *(Chris and Teresa are trying not to laugh.)*
Chris:	*(Pretending to be his mummy.)* Here you are darling… *(Chris takes his sock off)* …here are your eggies just how you like them, now open wide… *(Kev open his mouth and Chris rams the sock down his throat, Kev wakes up coughing, Chris and Teresa burst out laughing.)*
Kev:	What the hell did you do that for? That's minging!
Teresa:	Ahhh, lighten up Kev! We're sorry, did you want me to make you some eggies to say sorry? *(Chris and Teresa laugh.)*
Kev:	What are you going on about?
C & T:	Never mind.
	(Bianca and Tara enter in their dressing gowns.)
Tara:	What's all the bloody noise for?
Kev:	It's just this git thinking he's funny!
Chris:	Well it's nice to see that you are all so bright and cheery this morning.
B, K & T:	Sod off! *(They all collapse on the sofa.)*
Teresa:	Hey, where's Jay?
Jay:	*(From behind the sofa)* OH… MY… GOD! My head!

Section 10

(He pulls himself up over the back of the sofa. He is covered in streamers and has a stupid hat on, they all try not laugh and just stare at him.)

Chris:	Morning Jay. *(Chris and Teresa sit down. Chris has his arms around Teresa.)*
Jay:	Morning… what you all looking at?
Tara:	Nothing Jay, just go back to sleep. *(He collapses back behind the sofa.)*
Teresa:	So how come you all crashed here last night?
Bianca:	Too smashed to go back to our apartment.
Chris:	You had a good night then?
Tara:	Wicked! And you?
C&T:	Yeah, brilliant.
Tara:	Glad to hear it. *(She realises that Chris and Teresa are cuddling.)* Hang on a minute, you two didn't come home last night… does this mean?
Chris:	Yep, we are now officially…
Chris & Teresa:	A couple.
K, B & T:	Finally!
Jay:	*(From behind the sofa, he raises an arm in approval.)* Yeah about bloody time… Oww my head *(His arm falls down again.)*
Kev:	So I suppose you spent all night doin the wild thang did ya?
Bianca:	Kev!
Kev:	What?
Bianca:	You can't ask them that, it's not polite!… *(She starts to wonder)*… you didn't, did you?
Teresa:	B!

Bianca:	Sorry, curiosity got the better of me!
Chris:	Well for your information we didn't 'do' anything. We just had a super evening on the beach. Lying together, under the stars with the sound of the waves lapping against the…
Jay:	*(Still behind the sofa)* Will someone please shut that soppy twat up… he's making me feel ill!
Teresa:	Well I don't know what you lot are up to, but Chris and me are going to spend the day at the fair together.
T & B:	Ahhh… that's so sweet!
Jay:	*(Still behind the sofa.)* Right that's it! I'm going to puke!!
All:	Oh shut up!
Bianca:	Who's up for getting something to eat?
Tara:	Sounds good to me, I'm starving!
Teresa:	Right, well I'm gonna go get changed.
Chris:	Cool, I'll meet you downstairs in a bit.
Bianca:	*(Sniffing her armpits and coughing.)* I so need a shower.
Chris:	I'll see you lot later then.
All:	Yeah, see ya.
Bianca:	Don't do anything I wouldn't do! Not that, that leaves a lot!!!

(They all exit the stage except Jay. When they have all gone he pulls himself up slowly from behind the sofa.)

Jay:	Oh my head!

Section 11: Love Roller coaster!

Smoke fills the stage as soft red lighting fades up. A classical love songs plays as Chris and Teresa melodramatically run onto the stage from opposite sides towards each other in slow motion, arms outstretched. As he is running towards her, he trips and accidentally head butts Teresa, who falls to the ground.

Chris:	Oh my god, I'm really sorry! Are you OK?
Teresa:	I know I've always wanted a man to come and sweep me off of my feet, but that wasn't quite what I had in mind.
Chris:	I'm really, really sorry.
Teresa:	It's OK.
Chris:	How can I make it up to you?
Teresa:	Let me punch you in the face!
Chris:	What?
Teresa:	I want to punch you in the face, I think it's only fair, and by letting me do that, it'll show me that you really are sorry.
Chris:	Well… err… alright then?!?!
Teresa:	Right, you ready?
Chris:	*(Closing his eyes.)* Go for it!
Teresa:	OK. Here goes! *(Teresa draws back her arm as if to hit him and trusts it towards his face, stopping just inches away from him. She then leans forward and plants a kiss on him. Chris jumps back as if he's been hit.)*
Chris:	*(Shouting)* OUCH!
Teresa:	Ouch what?
Chris:	Um… nothing… you didn't hit me?
Teresa:	*(Laughing)* You should have seen your face! Come on, the fair is calling… you can take me on

"Lovers Leap".

Chris: What's that? Not a roller coaster is it, I can't go on roller coasters, they make me ill!

Teresa: No... it's like a love boat kinda thing, it'll be fine, come on.

Chris: OK, Cool.

(The lighting changes to a vibrant red and the sound effect of flowing water could fade up as Chris and Teresa line up to two blocks front centre stage to represent the love boat. Soft romantic music play as the ride starts.)

Chris: Now this is my kinda ride! Kinda relaxing really.

Teresa: And VERY private, so I can do this!
(Teresa goes to kiss Chris, but just before she does, she is interrupted by a siren and a voice over saying "Warning, Warning". This audio should be mixed in with the above track. The red lighting cross-fades to green. The serene love boat turns into a white-knuckle roller coaster. The rest of the cast rush on to stage and line up behind Chris and Teresa creating the impression of a full roller coaster.)

Chris: Teresa! What's going on?

Teresa: I... I don't know.

Chris: ...but... but I don't like roller coasters!... Oooooooooooh SHHHHHHIIIIIIITTTTTTTT!

(The music then fades up loud as the cast sways to and fro on the ride to depict the motion of the roller coaster. Chris is screaming throughout the ride. [To make this roller coaster effective, each member of the cast should only move when the person directly in front of them moves, with Chris being the one who controls the motion at the front. This will create a ripple effect through the roller coaster and will look

stunning!] The ride stops and the lighting and music returns to normal and all except Chris and Teresa exit the stage. Chris is frozen in shock and Teresa is laughing hysterically.)

Teresa:	Wow Chris, that was wicked! *(Pause)* Chris?
Chris:	I don't think I can move!
Teresa:	You OK? Come on, let's go somewhere else. You can try and win me a teddy from one of those machines… Chris?… *(Trying to pull him off the ride.)* Chris you'll have to let go of the seat! *(Pulling his arms.)* Chris… CHRIS!
	(The lights fade to black and they both exit the stage.)

Section 12: "E" who dares, wins?

Kev, Jay, Tara and Bianca enter, followed by Chris and Teresa who then jog over to meet the others. They are outside of a club. Quiet club music can be heard.

Kev:	Where the hell have you been?
Chris:	Sorry mate.
Kev:	We've been waiting here for ages.
Chris:	I was trying to win a teddy for Teresa.
Tara:	What for half an hour?
Chris:	Well… yeah
Teresa:	It was so sweet, he just wouldn't give up!
Jay:	Well I'm glad you're happy, but we've already wasted enough quality drinking time.
Bianca:	We all set?
Kev:	Right then…
All:	Lets 'ave it!
	(The music fades up as the lighting changes to a colourful chaser to signify they have entered the club.)
Kev:	This place is banging!
Teresa:	I love this tune!
Chris:	Now this is the kinda volume that music should be played!
Bianca:	And check out the totty!
Tara:	Tell me about it, I feel like a kid in a sweetshop!
Kev:	It's been a wicked holiday so far ain't it?
Jay:	Indeed!
Teresa:	Definitely!
Chris:	Damn right! *(Chris and Teresa kiss.)*

Section 12

Kev:	Ugh, get a room will ya!
Jay:	Who's up for working our way through the cocktail menu!
Teresa:	What! The whole menu?
Jay:	Yeah, there's only... 10 cocktails on here!
Bianca:	Bring it on!
Jay:	Well, you lot get them in, I'm just going to get some fags.
	(The lights fade to the side of stage as Bazza enters. Bazza is an old friend of Kev's and they haven't seen each other for a few years. The pair walk past each other then do a double take. This is followed by an over the top handshake and hug.)
Kev:	Bazza!
Bazza:	Kev! What the hell you doing here?
Kev:	I could say the same to you.
Bazza:	I'm working here over the summer mate, and loving every minute of it! You on holiday?
Kev:	Yeah, came over here a few days ago.
Bazza:	Here for long?
Kev:	Only a week so making the most of it.
Bazza:	Who you here with?
Kev:	That lot over there... oi you lot! This is my mate Bazza, we used to go to school together.
Bazza:	Hiya guys!
Chris:	Nice to meet ya buddy!
Bianca:	Small world eh?
Kev:	So, are you lot having a good night?
Teresa:	Too right!

54

Bazza:	Well your night is just about to get a whole lot better!
Kev:	What you on about?
Bazza:	Well as it happens I've managed to get hold of some mind-blowing gear!
Chris:	You've lost me mate?
Bazza:	Just check these babies out! *(Bazza delves into his pocket and producing a bag of ecstasy tablets. The bag of pills should be the only prop used in the play.)*
Tara:	Pills! What are they?
Bazza:	Only some of the best Ecstasy around.
Kev:	You beauty! Nice one Bazza. How much do you want for 'em?
Bazza:	Usually it's a tenner a pill, but seeing as you're a mate, 8 quid each.
Kev:	Nice one, give us six mate.
Bazza:	You're in luck! *(Bazza looks at the bag as if counting them and then throws it up in the air. The actors' eyes follow the pills in the air and Kev then catches them in his hand. The exchange of pills should be staged down centre!)*
Kev:	Sweet!
Bianca:	What are they like?
Tara:	Just imagine the best sex you've ever had and times it by ten!
Bianca:	Really! I'll have two then! *(She laughs.)*
Kev:	Easy tiger.
	(Both Chris and Teresa are handed a pill not looking sure about whether or not they should be taking them. Chris pulls Jay to the side.)

Section 12

Chris:	Mate, I'm not sure about this, I've smoked a bit of weed before but never pills.
Bianca:	You've got to try everything once in your life, that's my motto!
Jay:	Oh come on Chris, it'll be a great laugh! *(Pulling Chris to one side.)* Besides, you don't want to look a dick in front of Teresa do you?
Chris:	Well no, but…
Bazza:	No buts! Look, in 30 minutes time you'll be having the time of your life, I guarantee it!
DJ:	Good evening Club GFI. How you all feeling tonight?
All:	Wicked!
DJ:	Right, it's that time of the evening again, it's the Karaoke competition! So… get yourselves up here grab the mic and show us what you can do, and remember the winner gets free booze for you… and all your mates for the rest of the night!
Tara:	Hey that sounds like a laugh!
Jay:	If there's a night's free booze up for grabs I'm well up for it. C'mon Kev.
Kev:	Please welcome, the Karaoke King!
Bianca:	Come on!

(A medley of extracts of popular Karaoke tracks now follows. Tracks used in the original production were 'It's Raining Men' sung by Teresa, Bianca and Tara; 'Respect' sung by Chris, Kev and Jay and then finally 'Bohemian Rhapsody' sang by all six of the group. Torches were used during a blackout in the Bohemian Rhapsody section of the original production so as to imitate the original music video. These were held just below the actors' chins so that only their faces were visible.)

DJ:	Ladies and gents, we have a winner! Wait for it! The winner is… Bohemian Rhapsody sung by Kev, Jay, Tara, Teresa, Chris and Bianca. Congratulations guys, your free booze vouchers are waiting for you at the bar. Boy are they in for a good night!
All:	Result!!!
Teresa:	I am so going to need a stretcher home tonight!
Bianca:	Too right, it's cocktails for the rest of the night for me now!
Kev:	*(To Chris)* You still got that pill!!! Are you gonna take it or what?
Chris:	I'm going to, alright?… Just in a minute.
Kev:	Well make sure you do… they cost me 8 quid each.
Chris:	Alright! Look I'll see you in a minute, I need some fresh air. *(Chris walks over to the side of the stage and sits down.)*
Teresa:	Where's Chris going?
Jay:	Said he needed some fresh air.
	(The lights cross fade to the side of stage where Chris is sitting. He is sat looking at the pill Kev has given him and after a while he goes to swallow it but is interrupted by Teresa.)
Chris:	*(Talking himself into taking it.)* Come on Chris, just like taking a paracetamol *(Chris takes a deep breath and places the pill in his mouth.)*
Teresa:	Are you alright Chris?
Chris:	*(Spitting out the pill into his hand and hiding it from view.)* Yeah, just getting a bit hot in there, that's all?
Teresa:	Did you take it then?

Section 12

Chris:	*(Not wanting to look stupid.)* What… um… yeah, course I did. *(Looking down at his hand with the pill in.)* Why wouldn't I?
Teresa:	Oh right, no reason.
Chris:	*(Hoping she is going to say no.)* You gonna take yours?
Teresa:	*(Nervously)* Yeah, course.
Chris:	*(Nervously)* Cool. *(As he says the above line Teresa slowly drops the pill. As she drops it Chris looks at his, checks that she is not looking and throws it away. They freeze in a moment's silence. Teresa breaks this uncomfortable freeze by rubbing her arms as if she is cold.)*
Chris:	You cold?
Teresa:	A little.
Chris:	Come here, cuddle up to me. *(They cuddle up together.)*
Teresa:	You know… this is where we first kissed.
Chris:	Oh yeah, we've got to stop meeting like this, people might get suspicious! *(They both laugh. There is a pause.)*
Chris:	You know how much I like you, don't you?
Teresa:	Yeah… I think I do.
Chris:	I can honestly say that this moment, right now, has got to be one of the best times of my life.
Teresa:	Yeah me too… and there'll be many more.
Chris:	I hope so.
Teresa:	Yeah! *(The couple kiss and then freeze. The lights cross fade back into the club. Music fades up as they*

begin dancing. Jay is stood at the bar. The music fades out after a short while and they all make their way back to their seats. Jay is walking back from the bar miming carrying an arm full of jugs filled with cocktail, Chris and Teresa come running back over to join them.)

Jay: *(Behaving in a drunken manner.)* Ladies and gentlemen… your drinks are served.

Chris: Bloody hell Jay, you got enough there.

Bianca: Duh! It's free drink, might as well take advantage.

Jay: My mentisents exactly!

Teresa: Sentiments you mean!

Jay: Yep, them and all!

Bianca: *(Also behaving very drunk)* and look…
(To Kev) drum roll please Kev!
(Kev does a drum roll on his seat.)

Bianca: Curly straws for all of us!

Bazza: Ah wicked!

Tara: You know what, I think you lot have got to be the best mates ever!

Chris: *(Raising his jug in a toast.)* To mates!

All: To mates!

Teresa: May we all get completely shit faced and fall asleep in bushes!

All: To getting shit faced!

Chris: I must admit, when we booked this holiday, I thought we'd all just end up arguing, but you're all so cool.

Jay: Behave you soppy twat.

Kev: No, he's right! You guys are the best friends a guy could have. I could kiss all of you right now, and you know what I think I will!

Jay: Oh no you don't!

Chris: Oh come on, don't be shy.

(They are all laughing and acting drunk. Music fades up. The music should now play over the entire section that follows. A Mix of 'Spin Spin Sugar' was used in the original production.)

Teresa: Go on Chris get him!
(Jays runs away and Chris jumps on his back.)

Bazza: Oh I love this tune! Come on you lot!
Come and dance.

Jay: Get off me you Muppet!

Bianca: I'm way ahead of you!

Chris: *(To the others still on the floor.)* Come on!

They all jump to their feet and begin dancing; all except for Teresa who is struggling to sit up straight and is having trouble focusing on things. Her eyes start to flick about randomly. As the others continue dancing Teresa is sitting upright holding her head and behaving like she is extremely hot. Her jaw hurts and she begins rubbing it. Her eyes continue to flick around as she desperately tries to stand up, using a chair for support, however, she stumbles and falls to the ground. As she hits the ground, she vomits (the vomit was staged using a concoction of vegetable soup and various other ingredients which was placed in a bottle and hidden behind a block on stage. This should be stored in the mouth as soon as possible without the audience noticing, it was very effective!) and begins fitting in good view of the audience. As soon as she has collapsed all music should fade out completely, leaving only the vocal sounds that Teresa is making while fitting audibly. The sound of a heartbeat increasing in speed can be recorded and played over this section or could be made by the other cast members chorally.

Section 13: Coming down with a bump!

As the Heartbeat sound fx continues, the cast stack the blocks centre stage calmly and lift Teresa on top of them to symbolise her lying in a hospital bed. All exit the stage except Chris and Teresa. Chris moves to the front of the stage to address the audience.
NOTE: BE CAREFUL NOT TO OVER PLAY THESE LINES

Chris: *(Lines to be spoken as the cast rush around setting the stage as if it were a hospital.)*
One thing I guess you never really think about when you go on holiday is what happens if something goes wrong, and one of you falls ill. I'd never really thought about it. I remember Teresa being driven away in the ambulance. We had to follow in a taxi but none of us knew any Spanish. We needed to get to the hospital quickly but didn't know how to ask to get us there. Eventually after some frantic hand signals we got a taxi and arrived at the hospital, only to be greeted with more problems…

(Kev, Jay, Tara and Bianca run onto stage as if entering the hospital. Chris runs over to join them. They are trying to find a doctor that speaks English.)

Chris: Look, someone must speak English!

Jay: *(In frustration)* Shit!

(A Doctor enters. Chris sees him/her and runs over to speak to him/her. The doctor speaks in broken English with a Spanish accent. This should not, however, be comic in tone.)

Chris: Excuse me, do you speak English?

Doctor: Yes I do.

Chris: We're looking for a girl, she was brought here after collapsing at Club GFI.

Doctor: Ah yes. Who are you?

Chris: We are her friends.

Section 13

Doctor:	*(With a tone of sarcasm.)* FRIENDS? *(There is a slight pause as Chris realises that the Doctor is suggesting that maybe they are not as good friends as they could have been to Teresa.)*
Chris:	*(Said with guilt)* Yeah… I'm her boyfriend.
Doctor:	Your friend is not well. You know she take ecstacy, yes?
Kev:	Well yeah.
Bianca:	She's going to be OK isn't she?
Doctor:	We doing our best… You know where she got ecstacy?
Kev:	No.
Tara:	Kev!
Chris:	Yeah we do. *(Kev looks into the air and places his hands against his face as he sits down.)*
Doctor:	You must stay here; the police, they will need to speak with you.
Chris:	Where is she? Can we see her?
Doctor:	She is in intensive care, I take you there, but you wait outside, OK. *(The doctor exits followed by the group of friends. As they go to exit Kev grabs Chris by the arm and pulls him towards him.)*
Kev:	What's the matter with you?
Chris:	Get your hands off me? Look, I'm not going to lie for you Kev.
Kev:	Don't you get it Chris? Now I'm gonna have to tell them where I got them from and they'll do Bazza for supplying. Some mate that makes me.

Chris:	Kev, Teresa is lying in there unconscious… my girlfriend… your mate!
Kev:	And what do you think is going to happen to me eh? They'll lock me up and throw away the key.
Chris:	You what? Don't you think you should have thought about this before you started dishing out pills to your mates?
Kev:	Well I didn't see you complaining when you got them. You knew she was going to take it and you didn't try to stop her… I mean, you even took one yourself!
Chris:	But I didn't!
Kev:	What?
Chris:	I didn't take it.
Kev:	Well how come Teresa took hers then? I thought you went outside to take them together?
Chris:	Yeah we did…
Kev:	So she knew you weren't gonna take yours, but she took it anyway?
Chris:	Not exactly no….
Kev:	She took it first?
Chris:	Yeah
Kev:	And then what? *(Pause)*
Chris:	I didn't want to look…
Kev:	So, you made her think you did take it!
Chris:	Well no… it wouldn't have made any difference anyway, she'd already swallowed hers. *(Chris walks off to join the others who are frozen outside the room Teresa is in, trying to avoid dealing with the responsibilities being presented to him by Kev.)*

Kev:	*(Raising his voice as Chris walks off.)* Are you sure about that?... You hadn't taken yours!
Chris:	I spat it out.
Kev:	She didn't know that though?
Chris:	What are you trying to say?
Kev:	You know exactly what I'm saying.
Chris:	You can't blame this on me Kev... you can't... it's not my fault!
	(Chris and Kev freeze. The sound of hospital machines fade up, ventilators, heart monitors etc. The lights focus on the rest of the group as they stand huddled outside Teresa's room, looking through the window. The following lines should be addressed directly to the audience and build in intensity, reaching their climax just before the flat line sound effect.)
Bianca:	I'll never forget the look in her eyes... really wide and so scared, no... terrified.
Jay:	There were people rushing all around her and at one point they had to strap her down because she was convulsing so severely. I can't even begin to imagine what she must have been feeling, and I don't think I want to.
Bianca:	Screaming in pain... crying out... but there was nothing we could do... not now anyway. Nothing to do but just stand and watch.
Tara:	Her skin was so hot, really clammy! The doctors were saying that her temperature had risen to 109 degrees.
Jay:	She was covered in tubes, bleeding, blood seemed to be coming from everywhere, every needle puncture...

Tara:	And then I remember... just for a split second everything stopped! *(A flatline sound effect should play here.)*
Bianca:	From then on things went a bit mad.
	(Chris and Kev rush over to join the others. Two doctors rush into Teresa's room and as the following lines are spoken, they create various freeze frames to illustrate trying to resuscitate Teresa.)
Chris:	What's going on?
Bianca:	I dunno?
Tara:	She was shaking and screaming and then she, she just stopped.
Chris:	But why? Something must have happened?
Kev:	What have I done?
Tara:	*(Turning to Bianca who comforts her.)* I can't deal with this B!
Chris:	She's dying isn't she? *(To Kev with anger)* See what you've done! Tell me Kev, is this still your idea of a good night out? "You'll be having the time of your life" you said. Good old Kev, always up for a laugh... but no one's laughing now, are they Kev?
Bianca:	*(Covering her ears.)* Just stop it... please... just stop!
Jay:	She's not going to die alright! Look, someone needs to call her parents!
	(Chris, goes to walk back to the waiting room but is stopped in his tracks. The sound effect of a defibrillator can be used here as the lighting changes to a single spotlight over Teresa. On each thud of the defibrillator, Teresa's body should react as if being shocked and perhaps the single spotlight could flash down onto her as she does so, leaving

the others in darkness momentarily, and then return them to being lit.)

All: Defibrillator. Charging. Clear!
(Pause)

All: Silence.

All: Defibrillator. Charging. Clear!
(Pause)

All: Silence.

All: Defibrillator. Charging. Clear!
(Pause)

All: Silence… silence… silence… silence.

(At this point the lights should fade down to a single spotlight lighting Teresa's body. And another lighting Chris, the others exit the stage.
Chris produces a mobile phone and nervously punches in a number and places it to his ear with a heavy sigh.)

Chris: *(Quickly cancelling the call before anyone answers.)* …Fuck!
(Chris holds his head in his hands and tries to compose himself. After a moment he lifts his head to address the audience.)
What am I supposed to say? I know I have to do it but, how can I?… *(Pause)* …This is all such a mess. *(Pause)* I guess it wouldn't be so hard if we didn't know what went wrong, but we do… all of us… and that's the hardest thing to deal with… it needn't have happened.

(Bianca enters stage left also in a state of disbelief.)

Bianca: Chris, have you called them?

Chris: Not yet… I can't.

Bianca: Do you want me to…

Chris: No. It's the least I can do… where the hell do I start though B?

Bianca: Just start at the beginning.

            (Chris clutches his mobile phone and nervously punches in a number and places it to his ear.)

Chris: *(Nervously)* Hello?… Is that Mr Cookson?… Something's happened… I'm er… I've got something to tell you… about Teresa.

            (The lights fade to black.)

                        The End

Suggested cuts for 3m & 3f actors

Below appears a list of possible cuts to make the play work with 3m & 3f actors.

All supporting roles in this version have been cut. This will hopefully serve to make the play more accessible for students who wish to perform this as an exam piece. You may wish to make additional cuts in order to fit a desired timeframe; one suggestion for this would be to cut any choreographed sequences set to music.

Cut 1
From: Page 24: Where **Chris** says *"What?"*

To: The end of page 28.

Cut 2
From: Page 41: Where **Tara** says *"We're just going to the toilets…"*

To: Page 43: Towards the bottom where **Teresa** says *"OK"*.

Cut 3
From: Page 46: Where **Chris** says *"Well I wasn't expecting that…"*

To: Page 46: Where **Chris** says *"Alright then, you're on!…*

Cut 4
From: Page 49: Where **Teresa** says *"Well I don't know about you lot, but Chris and me are going to spend the day at the fair together."*

To: Page 49: Where **Jay** says *"Right, that's it! I'm going to puke!!*

Cut 5
From: Page 49: Where **Chris** says *"I'll see you lot later then"*

To: The end of page 52.

Cut 6
From: Page 54: Where **Jay** says *"Well you lot get them in, I'm just going to get some fags."*

To: Page 54: Where **Bianca** says *"Small world eh?"*

Cut 7

Page 55: The characters at the beginning of this page should be reworked as follows:

Kev:	Well your night is about to get a whole lot better!
Chris:	What are you on about?
Kev:	Well as it happens I've managed to get hold of some mind-blowing gear!
Chris:	You've lost me mate?
Kev:	Just check these babies out!
Tara:	Pills! What are they?
Kev:	Only some of the best Ecstasy around!

Cut 8

From: Page 55. Where **Kev** says *"You beauty! Nice one Bazza..."*

To: Page 55: Where **Kev** says *"Sweet!"*

Cut 9

Page 56: The line where **Bazza** says *"No buts! Look, in 30 minutes..."* This line should be spoken by **Kev**.

Cut 10

From: Page 56: Where the **DJ** says *"Good evening Club GFI. How are you all feeling tonight?"*

To: Top of page 57, after the **DJ's** speech.

Cut 11

Page 57: Cut **Bianca's** line *"Too right, it's cocktails for the rest of the night for me now!*

Cut 12

From: Page 59: Where **Chris** says *"Bloody hell Jay, you got enough there?"*

To: Page 59: Where **Bazza** says *"Ah wicked!"*

Cut 13

Page 60: **Bazza's** line *"Oh I love this tune..."* Should be said by **Tara**.

Suggested cuts

Cut 14

From: Page 61: Where **Chris** says *"Look, someone must speak English!"*

To: Page 62: Where the **Doctor** says *"She is in intensive care..."*

To make this cut work well, there needs to be some look or gesture of anger towards **Kev** from **Chris**, in order to set up a motive for **Kev's** line that follows.

Cut 15

Bottom of page 62: **Kev's** line *"Don't you get it Chris...* should be changed to *"Don't you get it Chris? Now I'm gonna have to tell them where I got them from and they'll do me for supplying!"*
Cut the sentence *"Some mate that makes me"*.

About ecstacy and drugs

About 10 young people die each year in the UK as a result of taking ecstasy type drugs.

If you wish to look into the issue of drugs and drug usage in more detail, or if you need any form of support or advice, the following contacts may be of help.

- **Addaction** (help in managing effects of drug/alcohol misuse)
  Tel: 020 7251 5860
  www.addaction.org.uk

- **Drug Concern** (parent and family support)
  Helpline: 0845 120 3745

- **DrugScope** (expert advice on drugs)
  www.drugscope.org.uk

- **National Drugs Helpline**
  Tel: 0800 776600
  www.talktofrank.com

- **Release** (health, welfare, legal needs of drug users and their families
  www.release.org.uk

- **The Centre for Recovery** (info and advice – special section for teenagers and parents)
  www.recovery.org.uk

- **Wotz da factz** (drug awareness for young people)
  www.wotzdafactz.co.uk

If you have enjoyed reading and/or working with this playscript, you may like to find out about other plays we publish. There are brief descriptions and other details on the following pages.

All plays deal with contemporary social and moral issues and are suitable for Youth Theatres, Schools, Colleges, and adult AmDram. They are ideal for GCSE Drama/English exam use and frequently do well in One Act Play Festivals. They offer both male and female performers equally challenging opportunities.

For enquiries or to order plays published by dbda, please contact:
dbda, Pin Point, Rosslyn Crescent, Harrow HA1 2SU.
Tel: 0870 333 7771
Email: info@dbda.co.uk

All enquiries regarding performing rights of plays by
Mark Wheeller, *Danny Sturrock* and *Johnny Carrington*
should be made to:
Sophie Gorell Barnes, MBA Literary Agents,
62 Grafton Way, London W1P 5LD.
Tel: 020 7387 2076
E-mail: sophie@mbalit.co.uk

All enquiries regarding performing rights of 'Heroin Lies' by
Wayne Denfhy, **should be made to:**
Wayne Denfhy, c/o **dbda**,
Pin Point, Rosslyn Crescent, Harrow HA1 2SU.
Tel: 0870 333 7771
Email: info@dbda.co.uk (subject: Wayne Denfhy)

Other plays published by **dbda**

ISBN 978 1 902843 20 9

Cast: 11+ (3m, 3f & 5 m or f)
*Suitable for GCSE with doubling
(2m, 2f & 1 m or f)*
Duration: 50 minutes approx.
Suitable for: ages 13+ or adults!

NEW! - KILL JILL by Mark Wheeller

Commissioned & premiered by The Birmingham Rep Theatre

Big Brother meets Kill Bill meets Jack (of Beanstalk fame) meets Tony Martin... This play by Mark Wheeller explores the topical issues of homeowners defending themselves and how far Reality TV should be allowed to go.

Jill is the latest victim of Reality Lottery, a futuristic form of National Service to entertainment. She accompanies Jack as he (again) robs George who lies in wait armed with a shotgun. The Reality Lottery camera operators are filming everything... but should they intervene?

'Kill Jill is a very fizzy ride! What a great script! The playfulness with style and wide range of reference points with an 'anytime, anyplace, anywhere' theatrical freedom... the banter goes to some strange places too – perhaps a Python influence? The build up of tension in the visit to George's castle put the end of the play in firm thriller territory! Wonderful stuff!!!!!'

Paul Mills, Head of Drama, Westgate School, Winchester

ISBN 978 1 902843 21 6

Cast: 2m & 2f
Suitable for GCSE
Duration: 55 minutes approx.
KS 3 & 4

NEW! - BANG OUT OF ORDER
by Johnny Carrington & Danny Sturrock

4 friends, 1 secret, 1 chance, 1 life.

Set on an urban estate in the UK, newcomer Ollie has a history of antisocial behaviour and is attempting to reform. His family are forced to move away in an attempt to make a fresh start... but once accepted into the local group of youths, things start to go wrong.

The play tackles the issues of anti-social behaviour head on, using a mixture of comedy, dance, music and multi-media.

'...the mixture of naturalism which pulls no punches, stylised movement, wit and mixed media, adds another dimension that certainly grabs the attention of the audience.'

*Fran Morley, Youth & Community Director,
Nuffield Theatre Southampton*

Other plays published by **dbda**

Too Much Punch for Judy by Mark Wheeller

A hard-hitting documentary play, based on a tragic drink-drive accident that results in the death of Jo, front seat passenger. The driver, her sister Judy, escapes unhurt (or has she?).

The tragic incident was dramatised by Mark in 1986 using only the words of those most closely involved and affected. This play has become one of the most frequently performed plays ever!

'The play will have an impact on young people or adults. It will provoke discussion. It stimulates and wants you to cry out for immediate social action and resolution.'

Henry Shankula – Addiction Research Foundation, Toronto

ISBN 1 902843 05 3

Cast: 2f & 2m with doubling or 3f, 3m & 6
Duration: 50 minutes approx.
KS 4 to adult

'The young audience I was sat in was patently out for some whooping Friday night fun... at the end there was a horrid silence.'

Nick Baker – Times Educational Supplement

Legal Weapon II by Mark Wheeller

This is a new "improved" version of the popular *Legal Weapon* play which is touring schools across the UK.

It is the story of a young man, Andy. His relationship with his girlfriend – and his car – are both flawed, but his speeding causes the loss of a life and the loss of his freedom.

In *Legal Weapon II*, the story takes an additional twist when Andy realises that the person he's killed is somebody very dear to Jazz, his girlfriend.

Legal Weapon II promises to be faster, funnier and far more powerful!

'A gripping storyline. Even the most challenging of our students were held by the drama. This learning experience should be given to each Year 11 as they come through the school.'

Myrtle Springs Secondary School

ISBN 1 902843 18 5

Cast: 2f & 2m with doubling
Duration: 60 minutes approx.
KS 3 & 4 and A Level

Other plays published by **dbda**

ISBN 978 1 902843 22 3

Cast: 2f & 2m with doubling, or up to 30
Duration: 70 minutes
KS 3&4

The Gate Escape by Mark Wheeller

The story of two truants. Corey is 'addicted' to bunking school. Chalkie views himself as a casual truant "no problem!" While truanting with some friends, the pair are greeted by a surreal 'Big Brother' figure who sets them a task. The loser will be in for some dramatic 'Big Bother'... Who will lose?... What will this 'bother' be?

The play has toured professionally throughout the south of England to great acclaim.

'A lively dramatic style and innovative structure with dynamic and contemporary dialogue. It is written in a way to guarantee that the audience will feel fully involved and enthralled by the main characters.'
  Professor Ken Reid, Author of Tackling Truancy in Schools

'Theatrically interesting... excellent basis for active discussion of issues and dramatic style with reluctant GCSE students'   *Ali Warren (National Drama)*

ISBN 1 902843 15 0

Cast: 8f, 7m and 2m/f
Duration: 70 minutes approx.
KS 3&4

Heroin Lies by Wayne Denfhy

A sensitive, yet disturbing look at drugs and drug dependency, in particular the pressures and influences at play on an ordinary teenage girl. We observe Vicki's gradual and tragic slide towards addiction and also the various degrees of help and hindrance she receives from family and friends.

This is a new, updated edition of Wayne Denfhy's popular play. It is suitable for performance as well as for reading in the class. Included with the playscript is an excellent scheme for follow-up work by Peter Rowlands.

'...a piece of drama that will stimulate and challenge a young cast... Heroin Lies deals with vital issues that affect today's youngsters in a gentle and humane way and, in so doing, gets its message across without the instant rejection that can meet other approaches.'

Pete Sanpher, Head of Drama, Norfolk

Other plays published by **dbda**

CHICKEN! by Mark Wheeller
New Updated Edition

A 'new and improved' version of WHY DID THE CHICKEN CROSS THE ROAD? The play tells the story of two cousins, Tammy and Chris. We are led to believe that something bad will happen to Chris who refuses to wear his cycle helmet. It is, however, Tammy who gets killed on the one morning that the cousins walk to school. Chris remains unwilling to tell anyone of his part in the accident and he has to live with this dreadful secret. One of the main changes is the introduction of Chris filming Tammy's fatal dare on his mobile phone camera.

ISBN 1 902843 19 3

Cast: 4m, 3f & 2m/f or 2m & 2f for GCSE
Duration: 35 minutes
KS 3 & 4

'We have just been fortunate enough to witness the most superb exhibition of interactive safety education. The performance was quite stunning!'

Jim Lambert, Head Teacher Sinclair Middle School, Southampton

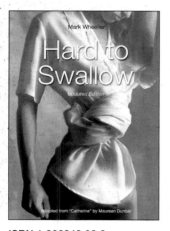

Hard to Swallow by Mark Wheeller

This play is an adaptation of Maureen Dunbar's award winning book (and film) **Catherine** which charts her daughter's uneven battle with anorexia and the family's difficulties in coping with the illness.

The play has gone on to be performed all over the world to much acclaim, achieving considerable success in One Act Play Festivals. Its simple narrative style means that it is equally suitable for adult and older youth groups to perform.

'This play reaches moments of almost unbearable intensity... naturalistic scenes flow seamlessly into sequences of highly stylised theatre... such potent theatre!'

Vera Lustiq, The Independent

'Uncompromising and sensitive... should be compulsory viewing to anyone connected with the education of teenagers.'

Mick Martin, Times Educational Supplement

ISBN 1 902843 08 8

Cast: 3f & 2m with doubling, or 6f, 3m & 16
Duration: 70 minutes
KS 3 to adult

Other plays published by **dbda**

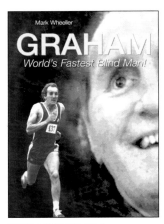

ISBN 1 902843 09 6

Cast: 5m & 4f with doubling, or up to 34
Duration: 80 minutes approx.
KS 3/4 to adult

GRAHAM – World's Fastest Blind Man!
by Mark Wheeller

A play full of lively humour telling the inspirational story of Graham Salmon MBE. Totally blind since birth, Graham went on to become the World's Fastest Blind Man running 100 metres in 11.4 seconds!

The play, written in Mark's unique documentary style, skillfully brings to life Graham's courage, tenacity and wonderful sense of humour. 'GRAHAM' was a finalist in the 2007 National Drama Festivals Association.

'GRAHAM was an ideal piece to challenge my group; it ticked all the boxes for A Level work. My Year 12 students who performed it as part of their AS Level did exceptionally well. All seven of them not only got the top grade for the performance but they were all awarded 120/120 marks!'

Mike Fleetwood, Parkside Arts College

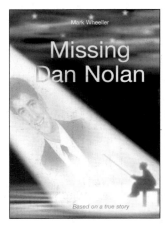

ISBN 1 902843 16 9

Cast: 2m & 2f with doubling, or up to 18
Duration: 45-50 minutes
KS 3/4 to adult

Missing Dan Nolan (based on a true story)
by Mark Wheeller

This play, based on the true story of Dan Nolan, a teenage boy who went missing on the night of January 1st 2002, is written in the same documentary style as *Too Much Punch for Judy*. It has won awards and commendations at every Drama Festival it has entered. It is now, like so many of Mark's other plays, being toured professionally by the Queens Theatre in Hornchurch, Essex.

'Unusual and deeply affecting. Skillfully written... achieves astonishing depth and authenticity... '

Charles Evans, Adjudicator, Eastleigh Drama Festival

'I feel very proud. All the issues about our Dan's disappearance, and the safety issues surrounding teenagers, are in the play and it will continue to raise awareness'

Pauline Nolan (Dan's mother)

Other plays published by **dbda**

WACKY SOAP by Mark Wheeller

Wacky Soap is a Pythonesque allegorical tale about 'substance' abuse (drugs, alcohol, glue, tobacco, etc). While washing with Wacky Soap leads to instant happiness and an inclination towards outrageous behaviour, prolonged use washes away limbs and ultimately leads to dematerialisation. This has become a tried and tested (and increasingly popular) School/ Drama Club/ Youth Theatre production and is an ideal vehicle for a cast of any age.

'Wacky Soap is a brilliant show for any age group. It has the "Wow factor" not the "Yawn factor" so often associated with educational material. The script is fast and comical. The songs are wonderfully catchy. The Audience at the end were calling for more'.

> Sally Dwyer, Hants Drama Teacher/
> Eastleigh Borough Youth Theatre Director

ISBN 1 902843 02 9

The full version of the Musical play which includes scheme of work for KS3/4.

The story of Wacky Soap first appeared as a full **Musical play**. A mini version of the play is included with the **Music Score**. The **Storybook**, as well as being a wonderful book to read on its own, is often used for inspiration with props and costumes for the play. A **Past-performance CD** gives you the opportunity to hear the songs of the play, while a fully orchestrated **Backing track CD** will be invaluable to those who want to produce the play but do not have music facilities.

ISBN 1 902843 07 X

A fully illustrated book with the story of Wacky Soap in narrative form.

ISBN 1 902843 06 1

*A companion book with the Music Score and a **Mini-Musical** version of the play.*

Past Performance and Backing track CDs